UE
Universal Edition
Universal

saxophone duets

for 2 alto, 2 tenor
or alto and tenor saxophones

für 2 Alt- oder Tenorsaxophone
oder Alt- und Tenorsaxophon

james rae

www.universaledition.com
vienna · london · new york

UE 16 551
ISMN 979-0-008-04281-2
UPC 8-03452-02374-6
ISBN 978-3-7024-2841-9

EASY JAZZY SERIES

The JAZZY SERIES was written to provide players of moderate abilities with experience of the syncopated patterns of jazz.

Now, the EASY JAZZIES offer this opportunity to players at an earlier stage of their musical development and provide a perfect stepping–stone to the abundance of solo and duet material in the main series.

JAZZY SERIES soll Musikern mit beschränkten technischen Fertigkeiten die Gelegenheit geben, sich mit den synkopierten Rhythmen des Jazz vertraut zu machen.

Mit dem Band EASY JAZZIES bietet sich diese Gelegenheit jungen Musikern nun bereits zu einem früheren Zeitpunkt ihrer musikalischen Entwicklung. Die Stücke stellen ein ideales „Sprungbrett" für das reichhaltige Solo- und Duomaterial der Hauptserie dar.

EASY JAZZY DUETS – SAXOPHONES *by* JAMES RAE

This collection of ten easy duets has been written to enable players of very modest abilities to tackle, without great difficulty, music in the jazz idiom. For ease of reading, the parts have been printed on separate pages. Chord symbols have been included at concert pitch to accompany both Eb and Bb instruments. There is also a separate Part 2 for Bb Tenor Saxophone if Part 1 is to be played by Eb Alto Saxophone.

N.B. In many of the pieces the quavers are to be played in 'swing–time':

i.e. ♫ = ♩♪ and ♫♫♫♫ = ♩♪ ♩♪

Diese aus zehn leichten Duos bestehende Sammlung soll dazu dienen, Saxophonisten mit sehr begrenzten technischen Fertigkeiten einen leichten Einstieg in die musikalische Welt des Jazz zu ermöglichen. Um der besseren Lesbarkeit willen wurden die beiden Stimmen auf getrennten Seiten gedruckt. Die Stimmen enthalten Akkordsymbole in Konzerttonhöhe sowohl zur Begleitung von Es–als auch von B–Saxophonen. Darüber hinaus enthalten die Noten eine eigene zweite Stimme für Tenorsaxophon in B, falls die erste Stimme mit Altsaxophon in Es gespielt werden soll.

NB: In vielen der Stücke sind die Achtelnoten im 'Swing–Rhythmus' zu spielen,

z.B. ♫ = ♩♪ und ♫♫♫♫ = ♩♪ ♩♪

CONTENTS

Part 1

SWINGIN' THE LEAD

James Rae

Universal Edition UE 16551

Part 2

SWINGIN' THE LEAD

James Rae

Part 1

BREAKOUT

James Rae

Part 2

❷
BREAKOUT

James Rae

ON THE MOVE

Part 1

James Rae

③

ON THE MOVE

Part 2

James Rae

TOO BLUE TO BE TRUE

Part 1

James Rae

Part 2

④

TOO BLUE TO BE TRUE

James Rae

Part 1

TWO CHORD SHUFFLE

James Rae

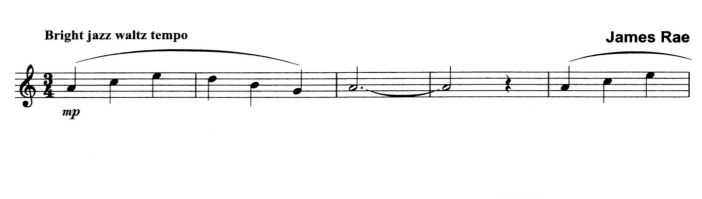

UE 16551

TWO CHORD SHUFFLE

Part 2

Bright jazz waltz tempo

James Rae

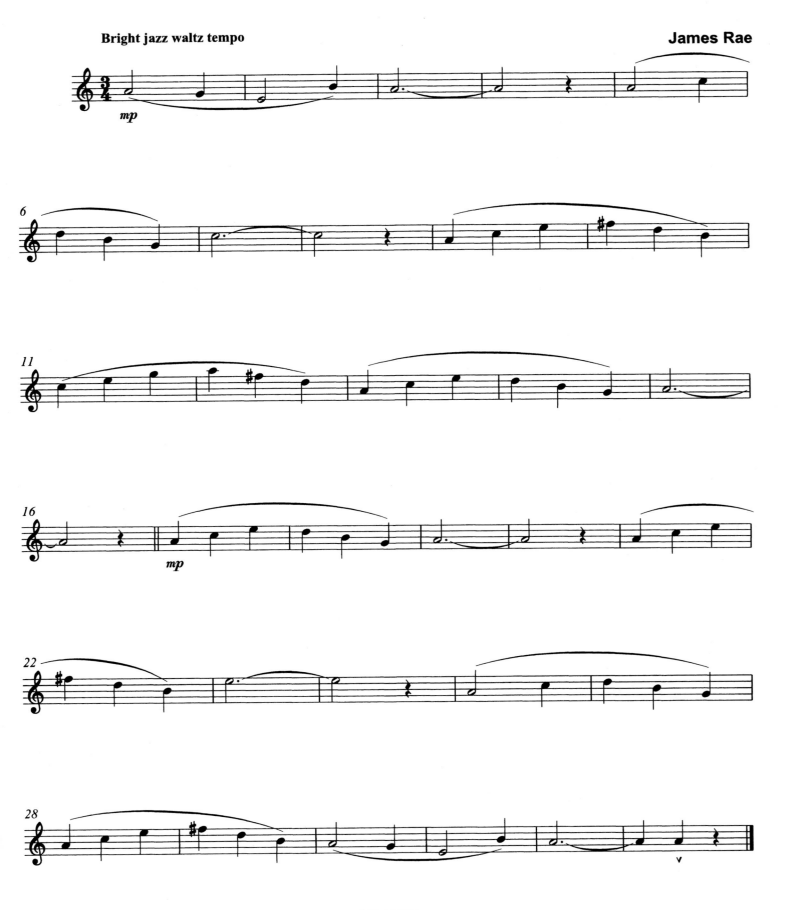

Part 1

FASTBACK

James Rae

Part 2

❻
FASTBACK

James Rae

UE 16551

TAKIN' IT EASY

Part 1

James Rae

Part 2

TAKIN' IT EASY

James Rae

⑧ GEMINI

Part 1

James Rae

Part 2

⑧

GEMINI

James Rae

⑨

AGAINST THE GRAIN

Part 1

James Rae

⑨

AGAINST THE GRAIN

Part 2

James Rae

GOODTIMES

Part 1

James Rae

⑩ GOODTIMES

Part 2

James Rae

UE 16551

JAZZY SERIES

18826	P. HARVEY/J. SANDS	JAZZY CLARINET 1
19361	P. HARVEY	JAZZY CLARINET 2
18827	J. RAE	JAZZY SAXOPHONE 1
19362	J. RAE	JAZZY SAXOPHONE 2
19393	J. RAE	JAZZY TRUMPET 1
18825	J. REEMAN	JAZZY FLUTE 1
19360	J. REEMAN	JAZZY FLUTE 2
18824	J. REEMAN	JAZZY PIANO 1
19363	B. BONSOR/G. RUSSELL-SMITH	JAZZY PIANO 2
18828	G. RUSSELL-SMITH	JAZZY RECORDER 1
19364	B. BONSOR	JAZZY RECORDER 2
19431	M. RADANOVICS	JAZZY VIOLIN 1
19757	M. RADANOVICS	JAZZY VIOLIN 2
16553	M. RADANOVICS	JAZZY CELLO 1
19711	T. DRUMMOND	JAZZY GUITAR 1
19429	J. RAE	JAZZY DUETS FOR FLUTES
19430	J. RAE	JAZZY DUETS FOR CLARINETS
19395	J. RAE	JAZZY DUETS FOR SAXOPHONE
19396	J. RAE	JAZZY DUETS FOR FLUTE and CLARINET
19756	M. CORNICK	JAZZY DUETS FOR PIANO
16536	M. CORNICK	JAZZY DUETS FOR PIANO 2
16537	M. RADANOVICS	JAZZY DUETS FOR VIOLIN
21395	J. RAE	JAZZY DUETS FOR RECORDERS

CHRISTMAS JAZZ

19184	J. RAE	CHRISTMASJAZZ FOR FLUTE
19186	J. RAE	CHRISTMASJAZZ FOR TRUMPET
19187	J. RAE	CHRISTMASJAZZ FOR CLARINET
19188	J. RAE	CHRISTMASJAZZ FOR ALTO SAXOPHONE
19189	J. RAE	CHRISTMASJAZZ FOR CELLO
19190	J. RAE	CHRISTMASJAZZ FOR TROMBONE
19185	J. RAE	CHRISTMASJAZZ FOR VIOLIN

www.universaledition.com
vienna · london · new york